Claire

Best wishes

Michael

My Life
My Hurdles

First published 2022

Illustration and design Cecily Salt
Back cover painting by Eliza Parker

Published under licence by Brown Dog Books and The Self-Publishing Partnership Ltd, Wick, Bath BS30 5RL
www.selfpublishingpartnership.co.uk

ISBN printed book 978-1-83952-435-6
ISBN e-book 978-1-83952-436-3

Printed and bound in UK
This book is printed on FSC certified paper

MIX
Paper from
responsible sources
FSC® C013604

For Eliza

My Life
My Hurdles

By Michael Parker

Illustration by Cecily Salt

A Graphic Memoir

Get over yourself. A catch phrase that couldn't be more apt for an Olympic hurdler with issues. These have been addressed and, to some extent, resolved in writing this memoir- my life's difficulties from childhood and ultimate success as an adult. From being sent to boarding school on my fifth birthday, to helping send the first Briton into space, this is the story of the hurdles I experienced, from World War 2 till world pandemic now.

Monday May 2nd, 1943

As soon as I wake up, I start crying! I've been crying off and on most of the night.

tap tap

I'm being 'sent away' to school.

I don't like this word AWAY!

AWAY!

I already go to school - SUNDAY SCHOOL! Where I listen to stories, play outside then come home to lunch of roast chicken & roast potatoes.

This new school is a very long way. Too far for me to come home again for a very long time!

After an hour or so we arrive at a large red brick house with tall chimneys near a main road, very different to my home. It has imposing pillars and standing on the steps is a huge man with a

...BOOMING VOICE called Mr. Curtis ((He says hello to)) my parents and...

What a splendid little fellow

Naturally I burst into fresh tears. With some loving words that I don't hear & a quick peck on the cheek, my parents quickly drive off.

Moments later I find myself in a huge forbidding entrance hall among lots of other boys many in tears as well.

God!

"Wa

Sniff

A woman comes up to me...
You must be Michael!
MATRON
Miss Collins.
I climb onto her knee and she reads me a story
It's my birthday today
I'm FIVE!
Happy Birthday Michael

Before that, my life had been happy, or so I believed. We lived on a farm deep in the Shropshire countryside.

My sister Mary was born to the sound of the only bomb dropped anywhere near us. I never heard it, just as I never saw searchlights in the night skies or woke to the sound of air-raid sirens. While the country faced food shortages, as German U-boats hunted down convoys from America, living on the farm we never went hungry.

My father, part of the 'Dig for Victory' drive, was tasked with ploughing up ancient parklands and bringing farmers up to speed on crop rotations, and the like.

I rarely saw him
as he criss-crossed the county
endlessly leaving my mother
alone to look after me, Mary and new
baby Gail, the farm as well as several
billeted evacuees.

Reaching school age, I could have gone to the local village school. The friends I played with at home all went there. I wanted to go too. The problem, for my parents, was that they were children of our farm workers. It might be unfair to label them snobs but, even in wartime, they were unable to escape the social pressure. They convinced themselves that sending me away to a prep school, Hurst Court, was the better option.

My mother, I learnt much later, was deeply unhappy about me going but was, if anything, more class sensitive than my father. She went along with the reassurances that I would settle down and enjoy being with other boys. And in some ways, she was right.

Halcyon
Roslyn Rd
6. 5. 44

Dear Mummy Daddy Mary and Gail
This is the very first letter I have written with a separate copy, so I hope you will not mind if it is not very long.
It was lovely coming back to school and seeing all the boys. We have had two games of cricket and I did enjoy it.

With lots of love
from
MICHAEL

After a few sad weeks, I begin to miss my mother less and less as my affections switch to Miss Collins, her starched aprons and bedtime stories. Before long days become almost enjoyable. We play games like tag and football, go on nature walks and treasure hunts.

Sunday is letter writing day. Our teacher is Miss Gopp. She is small and pretty with very bright red lipstick. Her whole face goes red when the sports teacher speaks to her.

The truth is I enjoy being at home AND school. I adapt to both. But at home, for days before the end of holidays, my happy world collapses as I face losing the people I love. Being told I would see them again in a few months is no help. I cry at the end of each holiday and at the end of each term. This goes on for two years. Then things change.

On VE Day, May 8th, 1945, the war ends. Over the summer, soldiers start coming home. I am home for the holiday. Our village holds a home-coming party in the ancient high street. It's criss-crossed with flags and bunting, lit up with fireworks, hunting bugles are sounded and the church bells peel all day. I am carried along by the emotion, laughter mixed with tears, everyone hugging and kissing everyone else. My mother, normally reserved, joins in. An enormous banner is draped on our lorry driver's cottage. He was called up when I was a baby. We excitedly crowd around him.

But I am still being sent away. Worse still the end of war means I will be even further distant.

My school, only an hour from my home in Shropshire, had relocated inland from the Sussex coast and the danger of invasion.

Now it is moving back, as mother said without irony, "To it's home town". That's ten long hours by train from my home.

Taking all day, they give me time to go through my emotional journey.

I still cry but not openly. I'm used to hiding my feelings

I'm sent like a parcel from home to school, then a few months later, back again.

Return to sender

But school wins out becoming more real than family life.

Even today, memories of it are clearer.

The teachers and matrons replace my mother and father.

I thrive, or was it survive, as I adapt to win everyone's approval.

My final report, aged 12, is a reminder of the main aim of preparatory boarding school. "He is the type of boy one can recommend without reservation to the authorities at his future public school."

My parents must have thought it was money well spent.

REPTON

Piercing yells come from inside my school house. This is my first day at Repton, and 1 have no idea what 'FAG, FAG!' means. The yard football we are enjoying stops instantly. All the boys race to the door. I follow ...

OMG It's Aitken The worst

Punishment at school is, however, something else entirely.

There is a variety of beating with varying degrees of pain! Most are administered by prefects. For lesser crimes, such as being late, the beating or 'flapping' is carried out using a gym shoe. Some prefects deliberately hit much harder than others. The bullies, who relish handing out the nastier fag tasks, enjoy causing pain. Aitken is a sadistic sod. He carves holes in the sole of his shoe so it emits a terrifying banshee sound as it swishes through the air to connect with my bottom.

This is nothing compared to the agony of caning. (Unbelievably, still in use in public schools until 1999. State schools banned it 15 years earlier.) At Repton, it is reserved for serious crimes, like pillow-fighting.

It's my first caning and my friends try to distract me. They know what's coming. In strides the prefect Aitken. "Parker, follow me!" In my pyjamas, I slowly make my way to the prefects' room. A number of other prefects assemble to watch.

"Right, Parker" says Aitken "bend over the chair."

Seconds pass. He makes me wait. Swish! The pain is shocking. I brace myself for the second cane. Swish! I bite my lip. Swish! I'm in agony and start to stand up. "Not finished! You're getting the full four!" I get up and leave the room, determined to hold back tears.

Caning is a rite of passage. I believe it gives me a certain kudos but not an experience I could share with my parents.

Apart from the hateful, but infrequent, canings my time was divided in three ways.

No.1 is my School HOUSE where I learn to fit in.

No. 2 is CLASSROOM time, mostly uninspiring, at best mildly engaging

No 3. THE SPORTSFIELD. Here is something I really look forward to.

Each year, we have sports day. Everyone takes part, aiming to achieve the 'standard' for their age group - running, jumping and hurdling.

The day before, I have a raging sore throat and am sent to the sick room.

I am feverish and hallucinating. In my fever, I have a vivid dream.

I am on a sports field. I am standing in a line of boys. I hear a gun. I race towards a hurdle. I fly over it as if I have wings. I fly over the next without hesitating. I am out on my own. I can't wait for each hurdle. My timing is perfect. I win by a mile.

I wake up, feeling better. I won't miss sports day.

I have never hurdled until now. I watch the races before mine and see how the boys run at the hurdles, stutter, stop, start again, slow down, hop, skip, jump and tumble. It looks very difficult. I start to feel nervous.

My name is called and, miraculously, I feel calm. My dream floods back to me.

The starting pistol fires.
I run flat out to the first hurdle. Without pause, I fly straight over it ...and the next ...and the next
my timing is perfect... I clear all the hurdles... I win 'by a mile'

What's that bull doing daddy?

Tell you when you're older

He never did!

CROSS POLLINATION (XENOGAMY)

SELF POLLINATION (AUTOGAMY)

SELF POLLINATION (GEITONOGAMY)

ANTHERS

STIGMA

FLOWER

STIGMA

INK

The Sex Impulse and Achievement

No. 20

SEXUAL BEHAVIOR IN THE HUMAN MALE

ALFRED C. KINSEY
WARDELL B. POMEROY
CLYDE E. MARTIN

The GUIDE through BOYHOOD

Compound Eye

Head

Antennae

Fore Wing

Legs

Pollen Basket

Hind Wing

Abdomen

Thorax

LIFE AND GROWTH

Supplementary Reader on Sex Education

C. M. LEGGE &
F. F. RIGBY

Birds
Bees

One summer, a prefect is expelled. No-one knows why. The gossip from the older boys is that he went 'too far' with a younger boy. I haven't a clue what that means but, I pretend I do.

Gradually, I learn more but no thanks to the school. Sex education is not on the curriculum. Nor anything else related to maturing physically or emotionally. Character-building is left to the playing field.

Words that change the course of my life. My housemaster persuades my father not to send me to an Agricultural college to follow in his footsteps. He always assumed I wanted to farm. I never knew how to tell him that farming was not in my blood.

"I can get him an interview at Cambridge". My father agreed. He liked to hear I was good at sport. I get into Cambridge but first, two years in the National Service.

National Service

My eighteenth birthday, 2nd May 1956, I sign up.

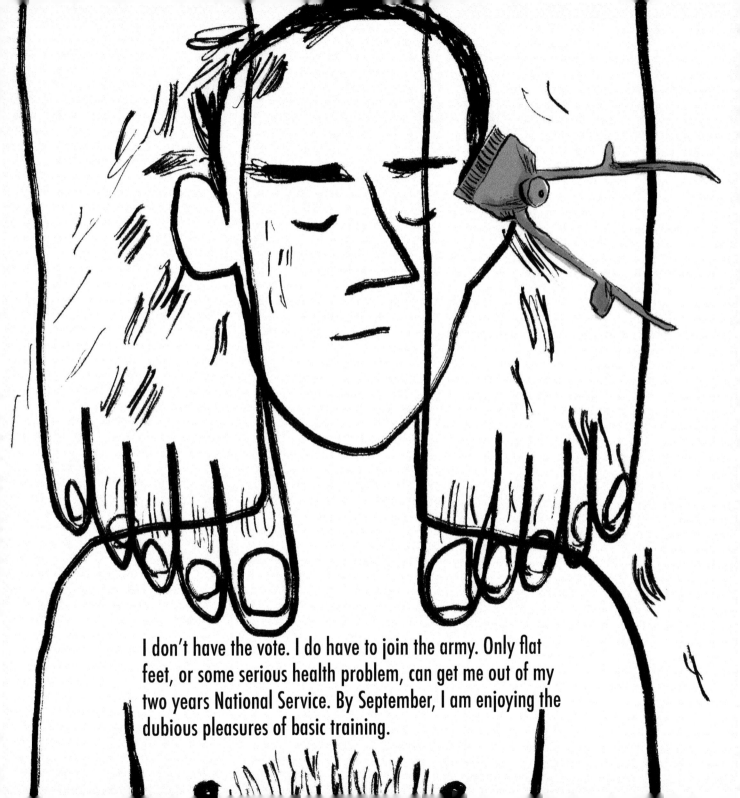

I don't have the vote. I do have to join the army. Only flat feet, or some serious health problem, can get me out of my two years National Service. By September, I am enjoying the dubious pleasures of basic training.

Catterick Barracks, North Yorkshire.
It is a godforsaken isolated place, miles from
anywhere, acres of parade ground and large barrack
blocks, surrounded by high wire fence.

It was built in World War I, and now 'houses' around 20,000 conscripts. Questions were being raised in Parliament concerning its total unsuitability for human habitation. I am virtually a prisoner.

The buildings we live in are grim, twenty to a room, iron beds, steel lockers, cold water and primitive toilets. We are confined here for the first six weeks and paid a princely 38 shillings a week.

Most of them have never been away from home before. 18 year olds sobbing quietly at night, missing their parents. Sobbing as I did when I was five, but not now. The army is just another separation.

For six weeks I endure the hell of BASIC TRAINING

RRRRr 4·30am

I wake before dawn, having slept poorly, as usual on the cement floor beneath my bed. (It saves making it each day and is the only way of having time to prepare for the rigourous kit inspection each morning.)

I fold each item of clothing to a precise dimension, checked by the duty sergeant. It takes hours. My made-up bed must also adhere to exact military specification. I mean exact, blanket folds to a quarter of an inch. Or else.

Shirts

10"

← 8" →

2"
←2"→

folded sock
(no edges)

For no other reason than a touch of sadism, the sergeant flings my neatly folded clothes on the floor.

You useless ****wit What are you?

I'm a useless Fuckwit Sergeant

Both army and school share the dubious view that humiliation is character building. The army sees "POLISHING' as a vital component.

I want to see my face in these

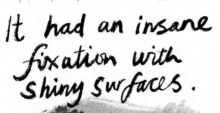

It had an insane fixation with shiny surfaces.

not naturally smooth

rough + pock marked

SIR YES SIR, Sergeant!

They must be turned into a mirror finish. I soon discover that everyday brushes and dusters will NOT meet military expectations.

Using a candle ...

I drip molten polish on to the boots then press, with the back of my spoon, to start the smoothing. I wait for it to cool, and harden, so I can start the process again, and again. (What a ****ing waste of time)

I don't see how this skill will make me a soldier.

The brasses are even harder to conquer.

I use sandpaper to begin the transformation.

I then apply Brasso

...wadding soaked in toxic ammonia based liquid

...I spend hours each night rubbing

My fingers are cracked and bleeding. One is swollen and throbbing. It is turning septic. I'm in agony. The sergeant is NOT sympathetic ...

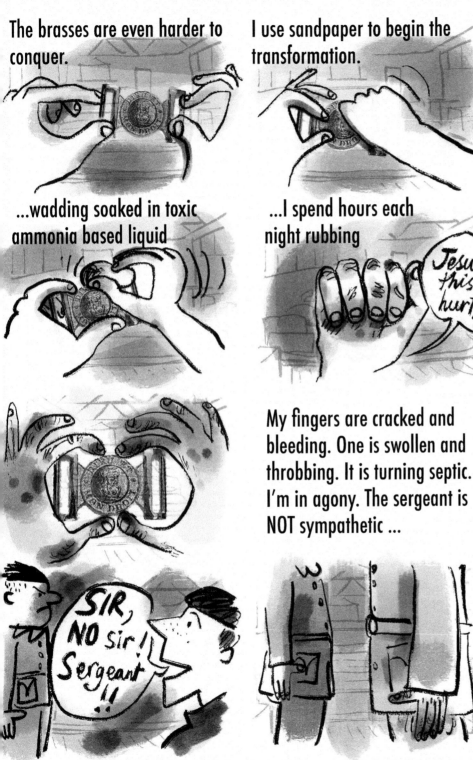

There is no escape from the routine humiliation. I go up to him for permission to go to the toilet.

I try not to look upset as he hands me three regulation sheets of toilet paper.

one up, one down, one for a polish

He seems obsessed with polishing but, basically, takes most pride in screamed profanity on the parade ground.

ATTENSHUN!

The first in the long running movie series 'Carry on Sergeant' was inspired by National Service at this time

My sarcastic bellowing sergeant is Aitken incarnate.

YOU'RE A F***IN MORON, Parke

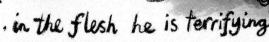

...in the flesh he is terrifying

He's taking it out on me because he knows I am the only recruit who was at a 'posh' school. He enjoys rubbing my nose in this. He knows I hope to become an officer.

This is where being a public schoolboy pays off. Preparing pupils to become officers is as important as getting them to university. My cadet training helps me face the formidable 'WASB', War Office Selection Board. For 3 gruelling days I face in-depth interviews, group initiative challenges, verbal and non-verbal reasoning tests and racing over obstacle courses (my favourite).

I pass into a different world from blea[k] Catterick to school in Aldershot. I swa[p] cheerless parade grounds for colleg[e] lecture halls. I am treated as an adu[lt] not a juvenile delinquent. The course [is] surprisingly well designed, combinin[g] class and practical military field wor[k.] I find the lessons on management an[d] personal development, never explored [at] school, perceptive and valuable. Se[x] is not covered. The army assumes w[e] know about sex. School pretends [it] doesn't exis[t.]

In a few short months I go from lowly boot polisher to being an officer, a second lieutenant. Loudmouth sergeants now salute me.

I join the 4th Queen's Own Hussars based in Germany.

It is an elite unit with a history dating from 1685. It celebrates Balaclava Day and was 'on the right flank' in the famous Charge of the Light Brigade.

Second Lieutenant
WINSTON CHURCHILL
4th (The Queens Own)
Hussars 1895

The elitist 'officer and a gentleman' lifestyle is expensive. Aside from working battle dress, I wear a Saville Row tailored service uniform complete with Sam Brown cross belt. My 'peacock' full dress uniform was worn at celebration events like Balaclava Day, and on parade at the changing of the guard. My father, unprepared but uncomplaining, stumped up about £2000 (today circa £30,000) the cost of my unsought badge of social status.

The officer's mess is a wonderful old hunting lodge, set in landscaped gardens. Dinner each night is a black tie affair, five gourmet courses, Georgian silverware, vintage port passed ceremoniously to the left before the ritual lighting of cigars. I am still only 18.

To complete this privileged experience, I have a batman to look after me, waking me with tea, laying out clothes, running errands and, best of all, cleaning my kit. I enjoy the benefits, but am not comfortable with this undeserved master-servant relationship, echoing my prefect-fag experience.

In my day job I am in charge of a troop of four Centurions, 50 ton state-of-the-art tanks, and some twenty men. But the real authority is my troop sergeant, a hardened veteran. I say 'Carry on Sergeant!' He does the rest.

ATTEN...shun!!

With his voice in my ear, I am ready for anything. One day it is silent ...

It's dusk as I arrive at the assembly point. The tanks are lining up in convoy for the twenty mile drive to Luneberg Heath - like Salisbury Plain an army training area - for our annual manoeuvres. The simulated battle exercise will be the nearest I get to real action. I am dressed in combat gear complete with beret pulled down over my left ear. I'm trying to look like the real thing.

My next task is to lead the entire squadron as it heads out. As troop commander, it is my job to get us to our destination. My map-reading skill is to be tested. I clamber aboard and squeeze into the turret that juts out above the hull of the tank. Only my head is showing. The silence is broken as some 30 tank engines start up. The noise is deafening.

Feeling very 'gungho' I give the order "Squadron. Move out!" The long line of tanks stretches behind me. I'm enjoying being in the lead. Until I take a wrong turn.

Radio silence is being observed. My indispensable sergeant is unable to warn me. I am taking the entire squadron down a peaceful suburban cul-de-sac. Tanks don't do reverse.

Rumble
Rumble.

The noise reaches a crescendo. One-by-one, 30 tanks make a U-turn. Brakes stop one track dead, the other accelerates madly forcing the turn, destroying neat German lawns.

Order is finally restored and we are ready to set off once more. My tank will now be in last place, not a position I enjoy. My embarrassment deepens as, in front of the watching troops, I report to the regimental Colonel. A hero in the war, when he was captured and held prisoner by the Germans, he is a legendary figure known to all as Loopy (Kennard). He is a throwback to the times when officers were gentlemen above all else. I envy his devil-may-care attitude.

"Parker! That was a monumental, glorious cock-up which will do wonder for troop morale"

CAMBRIDGE

I go to Cambridge fired up with athletic not academic ambition, uncertain about student life. I've swapped tanks for bikes, uniform for duffle coats, following orders to complete freedom. However, boys-only boarding schools, army barracks and a remote farm life have left me shy and socially ill-at-ease. Freedom? I don't know what to do with it.

At St Catharine's college, I am sharing rooms with a chap called Clive Oakley. Like me, a former officer. Unlike me, ridiculously confident and outgoing, so our sitting room is a must on the tea and crumpet circuit.

Clive keeps the social diary: punting on the 'backs', cycling to Granchester, going to the Arts Theatre to see Peter Cooke ('father' of modern satire) or visiting Cambridge theatre to witness the arrival of teenage pop idol Cliff Richard. Clive is close to his parents, regular visitors with home-made cakes.

I am not close enough to mine to have any dialogue to resist my future as a farmer. I am a reluctant student of modern agriculture practice that leaves me cold.

I feel alien, as I traipse along in wellington boots, on field trips pretending interest in livestock and plants I don't recognise.

Before my first term I visit a local track, in Wolverhampton, to check that my schoolboy hurdling prowess was real. When I go up to Cambridge, I want to live up to my master's claim, 'He's too good at sport!"

The track is virtually deserted. There are only two people there. One, a small man in a tweed jacket, is puffing on his pipe. He is holding a stop-watch. He is coach Bill Marlow.

The athlete, he tells me is Peter Radford, Britain's faster ever sprinter.

Feeling self-conscious I jog round the track

My 'magic' schoolboy timing deserts me.

I clear all the hurdles. I think I've done okay.

He beckons me over.

His quiet certainty convinces me he is the coach for me. Fortunately, he sees something in me, my hunger perhaps. He takes me on.

My first lesson is painful. Bill is right. I don't know how to hurdle. I have to unlearn my 'take-off and jump' style. I have to master the technique.

Bill is a coach and a teacher, one of the five top coaches in the country. He singles out one thing to focus on and makes me repeat the action over and over and over again. I learn fast. The track is more than my outdoor classroom. It is where I come alive, feel at ease and more 'myself' than anywhere else.

Selected to the university team, I am awarded my 'blue'. I strut around like a peacock.

The Varsity match against Oxford takes place at the iconic White City stadium. I win my first serious race.

More success follows. Within a year of my first session with Bill, I'm one of the leading British hurdlers. To my astonishment, the 1960 Rome Olympics are possible.

...if I can improve by just one tenth of a second, I'll qualify. That's the big if. That's the challenge.

I study less and train more. Chasing the time, I dash to any town hosting a competition.

Wolverhampton ...Milton Keynes ...Sheffield ...Birmingham ...inexperience, headwinds, poor starts all conspire against me!

My last hope of 'finding' that one tenth sec is at White City. It's now or never.

I WIN but to qualify all that matters is the time I clock.

WINNER MICHAEL PARKER
TIME 14.3 SECONDS

blame headwind on ending my Roman dream.

**** Rome!! It must be Tokyo in 4 years. I talk to Bill. He sees me as an 'accidental athlete'. I train just enough. I have a degree of natural aptitude but a gifted amateur is not enough. I need the attitude of an out-and-out professional - albeit unpaid.

Off the track, I'm very much the amateur with women, limited to the occasional daring cinema date.

Clive drags me to a party at a nurses' hostel.

I hover self—consciously, clutching a Babycham. One girl instantly catches my eye.

On a crackling gramophone Elvis Presley sings "It's now or never". I take heart and cross the room.

er, hi!

Light flirting moves to serious in no time. We kiss. 'So this is what it's like!"

We have nothing in common except physical attraction. Sue is a spontaneous free spirit, I am cautious, inhibited.

She is a pianist with dedication and talent that far exceeds mine as an athlete. She pours body and soul into her practising.

Her pursuit of her music, mine of athletics mean little time is spent together. She is finishing her studies at the Guildhall School of Music in London as I complete mine, earning my Batchelor of Arts Agriculture.

At the end of term, I go back to the farm and Sue returns to her home in Sussex. Once again, a long train journey separates me from someone I love.

The Farm

Yesterday I was a carefree student. Today I'm back in the farmhouse with my parents. I've been shunted between this farm and school or army or university since my fifth birthday. I now want to be anywhere but here. I'm like a mute prisoner unable to express these feelings. I resign myself to farming life.

Despite my BA (Arts?) Degree, I had learnt nothing. I still can't distinguish cabbage and kale. Numbly, I fall into the daily routine set by my father.

Farming is his passion, not mine.

It's misery. Up at dawn to muck out cattle, sometimes elbow deep inside a heaving ewe freeing its lamb, in freezing February harvesting sugar beet. With frozen fingers lifting the root, chopping the leaves with a machete, bent double all day long. Pure torture.

Farm-work every day and training every evening means very few chances to be with Sue.

WE DECIDE TO GET MARRIED.

Both our parents are dead against it. We are blind to the well-meant advice to give ourselves more time. We marry defiantly.

Sue is even less equipped to be a farmer's wife than I am a farmer. We live in an ugly Victorian house, a setting for Cold Comfort Farm. Numerous echoing rooms, mostly unfurnished. The only thing we added was an elderly piano.

Naturally gregarious, Sue is forced to spend her days alone. Both of us feel out of place, captives on the farm.

JUST MARRIED

I'm cold, wet, bored and miserable. The sky is overcast and grey.

Sleet is cutting into my face. The steel bucket seat is cutting into my bottom

I have no cabin to shield me from the biting wind.

I'm ploughing endless furrows, failing to keep them straight.

Three days in the same field means a lot of thinking time.

Like the furrows of soil, my mind is churning.

As I start the hundreth furrow of the day, I stop.

Enough.

After months of prevaricating, I have decided.

I AM NOT
A FARMER!

I get down from the tractor and squelch across the ploughed soil to the farm. I announce my decision. Sue is delighted. My father's reaction takes me by surprise. He and my mother have apparently long been deeply concerned over my farm unhappiness. It's a shame we couldn't talk to each other until this point.

He puts aside what must have been a huge disappointment and is kind and generous in trying to help me find a different future.

With no idea what I might do, I talk to my college tutor for advice. "I suppose you could try advertising." He makes it sound like a last resort. He arranges an interview with a London agency and I jump at the job offered.

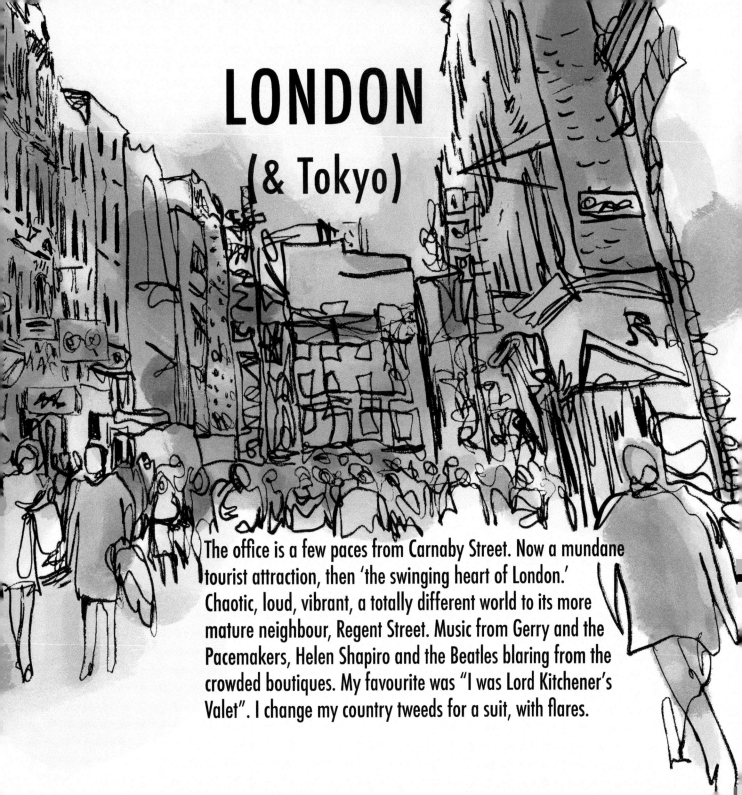

LONDON
(& Tokyo)

The office is a few paces from Carnaby Street. Now a mundane tourist attraction, then 'the swinging heart of London.' Chaotic, loud, vibrant, a totally different world to its more mature neighbour, Regent Street. Music from Gerry and the Pacemakers, Helen Shapiro and the Beatles blaring from the crowded boutiques. My favourite was "I was Lord Kitchener's Valet". I change my country tweeds for a suit, with flares.

Sue is now pregnant and we need a proper home. Not easy on my annual salary of £550. I'm saved by my father who steps in to help me, as I go my way not his.

His generosity allows us to buy a flat in Hampstead. The leafy heath reassures my mother we will at least see a tree through the London smog.

She views as equally dreadful the world of advertising. And at the start she is right. Run by ex-officers who served in the war, military thinking is applied to the agency's basic training.

My degree, experience as an officer and athletic success count for little in the mail room, or as print machine operator, typesetter, proof-reader or in despatch lugging heavy print blocks to Fleet Street.

The challenge is boredom and long hours. I train late each evening and I hardly see Sue.

I'm not given time off to compete. For one match, against Germany, this means I almost miss the match.

Changing into my kit in a mad taxi ride, I arrive but with no time to warm-up. Amazingly, I win.

Finally, I'm entrusted to a piece of business, The Milky Bar Kid, with his irritating jingle "the milky bars are on me." He will be my companion at work for several years.

I feel it's acceptable to claim: "he is tough and strong ...only eats what's right ...just can't go wrong." If smoking is good for you, why not chocolate.

CRAVEN "A"

Will not affect your throat

I was not surprised by Dusty Springfield's hit: "Wear your hair just for him. Do the things he likes to do."

LADIES' DEPT.

What she looks for—

MAINLY FOR MEN

What he insists on—

Together you'll choose a MORRIS OXFORD

You mean a <u>woman</u> can open it?

You'll be happier with a HOOVER

THE HOOVER COMPANY

My innocent question "Whose secretary are you?" Is met with scorn. She is a Research Manager. It had not dawned on me that women had real jobs.

The Chef does everything but cook – that's what wives are for!

In these days, 1962, it's acceptable to say "The Kenwood Chef does everything but cook ...that's what wives are for."

show her it's a man's world

Van Heusen

man's world

ties

I do not assume or believe my wife should work. At near concert level, she spends most of her day on the piano.

She is driven by the pursuit of perfection, rather as I am driven, after work, in my athletics.

She always finds time for Julian our son, whilst I start excusing a growing distance between us on the twin pressures of work and hurdling.

Deeper than this is my fear of intimacy, keeping emotion at arms-length. I avoid confrontation and fail to respond to Sue's natural need for reassurance.

With huge reluctance Sue accepts we should divorce. To avoid the guilt and sense of failure, I train relentlessly.

A break from training brings an epiphany moment. I accept with some trepidation an invitation to the Royal Opera House for my first ever glimpse of ballet, Giselle. Not high on a farmer's agenda.

I find the 'corps de ballet' mildly engaging, then as the stage clears, the audience draws a collective breath, the music lifts and a single dancer in brilliant white, bounds into view ...

...leaps explosively, elegantly, impossibly, around the stage again and again. It's Rudolf Nureyev

Ballet Rambert

Who do you think you are Rudolf Nureyev!? Ha HA!

A spellbinding dancer, but I'm more inspired by his athleticism. I enrol for ballet classes the next morning.

Self-conscious, I join a class of twenty young female students in tutus. "I'm here to help my athletics"

They are unimpressed. Drilled from childhood, their bodies know how to move in a way mine doesn't.

second and ... in ... and out ... and continue and stretch ...

At the barre, Madame Nina, less forgiving than any coach, gets to work on my plié and my arabesque.

The wall mirror reflects my clumsy efforts. "Gardez la position!" "Tenir et relax" and too often "pas comme ca, refaites encore!"

She is terrifying. I start to understand the remarkable discipline and control required. As a result of these classes, I am a better hurdler.

Nureyev fled from Russia. I'm here to compete in Volgograd, previously Stalingrad 'the largest bloodiest battle in the history of warfare.' Just eighteen years later, my tour guide Tanya recalls the horrors.

Standing in the rebuilt railway station, she gestures dramatically "Russian soldiers here one day then German b*******, then Russians then German b********. In the course of the battle it changed hands thirteen times!

Unlike that battle, my race nearly ends before it can begin. A deluge turns the track into a river but the same resolute Red Army come to the rescue. They flood it with gasoline, then set it alight to create a vast ring of fire.

It is surreal! The cinder track is almost too hot to touch. Pungent fuel vapour makes breathing impossible, nightmare conditions for a race. Against expectations, mine and everyone else's, I win. As a team, we defeat the mighty Soviet Union.

Late night vodka celebration leads to early morning departure for Budapest. Delayed by a hurricane, we spend hours on the tarmac in a shuddering elderly Ilyushin jet. Too emotionally drained to sleep. For the first time in my life, I am dreading a race.

I arrive early at the deserted warm up track, cold and shrouded in mist. Listlessly, I start stretching exercises. I'm already feeling tired.

Out of the mist a 'woman in white' ghosts into view, an athletic angel, long blonde hair flowing, she moves like a dancer.

She joins me jogging round the track, her name was Shia. We chat for minutes only but I will always remember our brief encounter.

She has lifted my spirits. I enter the stadium in what seems like a state of grace. I have never run so well. "Poetry in motion", says coach Bill later.

BANG!

It's my fastest race, a UK record that stands for 6 years. My time is 13.9 seconds. I'm the first Britain to break the (then) magic 14 second barrier. See for yourself, search YouTube 'Athletics-Hungary GB 1963' 30secs

Tokyo Olympics '64 is now my aim. I intensify my winter training. Every evening after work I attack the deserted hills on Hampstead Heath, sprinting uphill between dimly lit lamp posts, on rough tarmac paths often icy or snow-covered. The self-inflicted pain pays off. I QUALIFY!

Life is extraordinary. For two weeks everyone lives their dream, adrenaline-high, feet not touching the ground. We are performers, waiting for the curtain to rise on the world's biggest stage. It's show time!

Today's the day. The warm-up track is crowded with 'gladiators' of which I am one. At first unnerved, I soon feel in my element. I can't wait to race. I must finish in first three to qualify for the semi-final. I'm in a trance, oblivious to my surroundings. So totally focussed that the stadium might be empty for all I know. There were 60,000 spectators.

I am oblivious to the gusting head wind, sleeting rain driving into my face. ON YOUR MARKS. Utterly composed. GET SET. Concentration 100%. GUN!! I react first. I reach the first hurdle first. I reach the finishing tape first. I run the race of my life. I am an Olympic semi-finalist. On that day I am the fastest hurdler in the world.

TOKYO 1964

The next day, I fail by inches to reach the final. I am devastated. Yesterday the fastest. Today an also-ran. One tiny error cost me my dream. Like Greta Garbo I want to be alone.

But not for long. In a friendly bar I meet Satchiko, a demure bar girl. She speaks not a word of English, me not one of Japanese. Aided by a phonetic dictionary I say 'Kireina' (you are beautiful)

Later, I try something bolder "Watashitachi wa shizukana basho ni ikimasu" This, I think, means 'we go to a quiet place?' Her expression gives little away but when the bar is closed we set off walking the deserted early morning streets. She tiny in full Geisha kimono, me in my British track suit. The quiet place is her flat. Spending two weeks there is the best possible therapy. We are sad to say 'sayonara' the only word we both understand.

Viva Mexico

Tokyo was the experience of a lifetime. I want more. In the office I tread water as a mild-mannered Clark Kent. On the track I am Superman. I zoom across the Atlantic to compete for the Commonwealth against the USA. I penetrate a vast bunker in Dortmund to win silver in the European indoor championship. Finally, with a single bound I land in sunny Jamaica.

The 1966 Commonwealth Games coincide with a week long celebration of Independence Day. Kingston reverberates night and day to the sound of Toots and the Maytals festival song "What a Bam Bam".

My rival is David Hemery (Gold, 400 hurdles, Mexico '68) His coach inspires him with poetry

...about me.

"David you must run FASTER, The man to beat is Michael PARKER!"

It works. He wins gold to my silver. Second is nowhere.

The carnival is over. I am facing a tough choice. Hurdling still a passion but age is against me. Broadcaster David Coleman calls me: "The veteran, evergreen, Peter Pan of athletics"

"...The veteran evergreen Peter Pan of athletics"

I can no longer sacrifice my professional career to my amateur one.

Clients, not my favourite people, must come first, training second, squeezed into late evenings. After several near misses, I have one last-chance qualifying race for Mexico selection.

It's now or never. I break the tape first, absolutely convinced I've won.

The blazer clad judges study their stop watches. They disagree. "Winner ...Storey ...time 14.1 (qualifying time) Second place ....Parker ...... time 14.2

I PROTEST LOUDLY. To my astonishment, normally unyielding officials declare the race can be re-run.

I HAVE MISSED ...QUALIFYING !!!

Can we have a re-run ??

spectators will enjoy the extra excitment

The starter calls us to our marks. I have never ever felt so determined. Perfect start. Perfect race. Again, I know I have won. This time the judges agree.

FIRST PLACE PARKER, time 14.1 seconds

... ...I am going to Mexico.

mexico 68

Jamaica had put on a street party. Mexico is showing off to the world.

The superb identity (best ever) is everywhere, stadium, streets, shops, bars, flags, bags, T-shirts, sombreros, the city is embracing the Games.

MEXICO68 ano de la REPRESION

(I don't learn till later of massacred students. "We don't wan't Olympics, we want Revolution!)

The first round of heats is my last. Four years ago, I was among the top ten hurdlers in the world. Today, I am a has-been.

My best is no longer enough, getting to Mexico was the goal. I will make the most of it.

A small consolation.
I had not exactly been the 'face of the Games' but am almost recognisable as I hurdle over the famous identity. Not winning my heat. The poster was used internationally to promote the film of the Games before colour television was in every home.

JEUX OLYMPIQUES MEXICO

As a spectator I witness history being made. "The Star Spangled Banner" strikes up. On the podium, head bowed, stands Tommie Smith, 200 meter gold medalist, black gloved right hand raised. Beside him John Carlos, bronze, left raised.

I'm awed by their defiance and bravery. One of the iconic images of the twentieth century.

Now the track events are finished, I have three weeks before returning to London. I have met Cyretta, one of the team translators. She has become my personal guide to the city, its culture, music and food. I'm not sure which of us more easily persuades the other but we are soon heading to the Acapulco coast.

We travel in her small old car. 250 miles of dusty roads winding between cane fields. The peasant workers in ubiquitous baggy white coats, wielding machetes, remind me of scenes from the movie Viva Zapata, with Marlon Brando as the legendary revolutionary.

We spend two weeks at a stunning almost deserted bay. Unbelievably blue sea, a ramshackle bar and our own bamboo hut. We share the beach with a few wild pigs. Paradise.

ACAPULCO

I promised I would and I meant it. Instead, I use distance as a way of avoiding commitment or closeness.

Airline Adman

I feel nervous meeting my new client.

Terry Coates, advertising manager proves to be the 'dream' client. Infectious enthusiasm and a boyish optimism.

He is always looking to say 'yes' to new ideas. His instincts are sound and, like my coach Bill, he brings out the best in me. And the agency.

This results in eye-catching posters launching the VC 10 airliner. "Love at first flight" and "Try a little VC tenderness"

A television campaign boasts an award winning commercial by the young Ridley Scott.

A costly 747 commercial featuring Verushka, the world's tallest model, never runs. The pilots go on strike. Never a dull moment in the world of advertising.

I take a Concorde test flight. I leave Heathrow at breakfast, take coffee in Canada, tea back at the agency.

As our poster says, I do "Arrive in better shape."

I am looking at rows of headshots of new staff. One stands out! A back shot in a white bikini!!

New Staff

Intrigued at the sheer audacity of submitting such a profile picture, I rove the corridors to check out the newcomer, Eliza. We meet again, (accidentally!) in a crowded bar. She asks, "Anyone going my way?"

"YES." I say

Her way means two hours in the wrong direction. Time for the first of many probing questions.

why does everyone say - whatever you do, don't go out with that mike parker!

Advice from her 'well meaning' creative colleagues backfires. Eliza wants to find out 'why' for herself.

My well-practised evasion of personal questions is soon undermined. Her ever-ready arsenal of humour and devastating directness soon threatens my defence.

The Suits

We are like two contestants in a duel. My lunges are no match for her lightening ripostes. Often our piste is the office where we are a spectator sport for two 'warring' groups.

Eliza is a junior copywriter, one of a handful of women fighting for acceptance in an undeniably sexist creative department. I am a "suit" in account management. Both sides view the other as a necessary evil. As our jousts go on, other differences emerge, not least personalities. "I just dont know what I see in you." She sees something, that's all that matters but my deep wired emotional distancing armour is still in place.

The wonderful world of the P&O Cruise Liner

I'll do anything to escape...

A typical thrust from Eliza breaks through. Miserable, while stuck mid-Atlantic on a writing assignment, with geriatric passengers her only companions, she badgers the Captain to allow a ship-to shore call.

Brring!

...Marry me!

... ...how can I say no?

Heaven at home is now marred by hell at work. If Terry was my white knight, his replacement is my nemesis, the dark knight.

Cautious and dour, his default response is to find fault with each idea I present.

Each 'no' I take as a personal rejection. My confidence suffers. I feel as powerless and insecure as I was with my father.

I am fired!

My first failure since failing as a farmer twenty years ago.

I compound the error by joining an agency best known for nurturing 'relationships'. Wining and dining and socialising with clients is not my forte.

aaagh
failed again
I am a failure!
THE IDIOTS!
Why dont they get me?
Why does this keep happening?
I DON'T KNOW WHAT IS WRONG WITH ME!!!!
Grrr...
Come on! Something else will turn up!
!! full on Shame attack.

And so it does .. I get a timely call from Saatchi.

Saachi & Saatchi

It is the only agency everyone talks about. Black cab drivers know the famous Charlotte Street address, the man in the street has heard of them. So has the woman in the countryside. My mother is reassured by the 'Tory Party' connection.

CEO Tim Bell, Margaret Thatcher's favourite adman, said "We were impressed with the way you pitched against us last year. We want you pitching for us" Perfect. This appeals to me.

"Will you join us?"
"When can I start?"

The agency competitiveness flows from Charles Saatchi. I first glimpse it on the tennis court. Not naturally talented, he arms himself with the largest permissible racquet and stands menacingly close to the net, defying attempted passing shots. In the agency, he is a force field spreading collective self-belief.

He tasks me with the impossible, to persuade BA to pay for the most expensive commercial ever. "Reducing the cost is not an option."

My 'budget' pitch is successful. 'Manhattan Landing' gets made and is rated one of the best commercials of the 20th Century.

The bold claim, 'British Airways. The World's Favourite Airline' demanded bold advertising. (Every year, BA passenger numbers across the Atlantic equated to Manhattan population.)

One of the best press advertisements of the century starts with a call to reception. General Dinayev is like an early Bond movie villain, beetle browed, Slavic features, an intimidating figure.

Our conversation, through an interpreter, is punctuated by him rubbing thumb and forefinger together, the universal sign for money. He wants lots of it, and he wants Saatchi to persuade Coca Cola to pay him to paint their iconic bottle on a Soviet rocket heading into space. A truly imaginative global branding idea ... until we discover the iconic image would not survive blast -off.

Two days after our meeting he is expelled in a tit-for-tat spy exchange.
Two years later he re-appears, this time with some cash and with possibly the strangest brief ever, "I want Saatchi to find the first Britain to go into space." We accept his bizarre challenge. I love the notion of being part of the space race.

ASTRONAUTS WANTED
* no experience necessary

How do we pinpoint one individual from 60 million, for a project no one has heard about, (we dub it Project Juno) from a country until recently behind an iron curtain?
The inspired creative team crack this complicated task by writing a simple recruitment advertisement. And then run it once as a full page in every national newspaper.

It generates a staggering 13,000 replies. After two years of training Helen Sharman becomes the first Britain in space.

The biggest pitch of the century starts when I help the Arts and Sports Councils lobby for a lottery with a survey of public opinion. "Would you have a flutter for a good cause?" YES!

hmmm

I present the findings to 200 journalists, half from back pages, half culture. The coverage helps persuade PM John Major. The race to be the first national lottery operator is on.

Saatchi backs the winner of six competing consortia, Camelot. I head up the team to launch the first lottery in Britain since 1876.

Script

The campaign introduces the, now ubiquitous, crossed fingers logo.

The National Lottery®

On television, a giant finger scours the nation.
Thirty million earthlings buy a ticket.

I never bought a ticket, but fortune is on my side. Eliza's warmth and wit are both support and inspiration. Already the proud father of a son, Julian, I now have two daughters, Laura and Hannah. And I am a delighted if over-protective dad. Split tennis balls cover every sharp corner.

TEAM

What next? As the euphoria of the lottery win fades, I miss the thrill of the chase and Saatchi has lost the 'nothing is impossible' spirit. I seize the opportunity to launch a new lean, mean, diet version of the agency. I call it Team Saatchi. The name reflects the informality and lack of hierarchy I want, not my nature. My sporting success was as an individual, not at ease joining a group as a team player. I am better at leading.

We set out to attract entrepreneurially minded clients who enjoy feeling part of a team, working together in a creative workshop. We transform the scruffy office area assigned to us.

We ask upcoming graffiti artist Temper to treat the entire office as his canvas, walls, doors, lifts, stairwells, ceilings. Over the weekend he creates 80 feet of electric eye-popping mural.

We pitch ceaselessly. (I am hurdling everyday) We pitch for any brand that excites us. We pitch for any client with an intriguing idea (almost) regardless of budget.

We introduce Cobra as the 'beer from Bangalore'. For an innovator with no cash, we planted road signs. He went on to create Fever Tree (and now has money). For an entrepreneur who came to us with an idea for a payment service, we named and launched it, (now in 17,000 shops). For the BBC, we promoted classical music to drivers. We branded the original love island, Cyprus.

BBC RADIO 3 DRIVE TIME. 90–93 FM.

Retirement ends my years at Team Saatchi, the best in my life as an adman. I have done things my way, creating my own playing field.

COACHING

"What now, what next?" Eliza sympathises, but only a bit. "Take a course, photography, creative writing ... anything to fill the void." None appeal.

We want you to be our pitch coach.

Mike it's for you

Sounds perfect

The call is from CBRE (No.1 real estate firm).
"We want to win more pitches!"
They need coaching.

I have not coached before. My only experience comes from being coached by Bill. He taught me how to hurdle. He gave me the self- belief to perform under pressure.

I know how to pitch. I've done nearly a thousand of them but I still suffer from the 'worse than death' fear of public speaking. If I can't crack this, I won't inspire confidence.

To overcome my 'fear', I set out to become an on-stage performer. I scour books on acting and talk to actors.

I study endless TED Talks.
I learn from Aristotle and Demosthenes who taught the world the art of rhetoric.
I am intrigued to discover that athletics and rhetoric were regarded as 'twin arts' in bodily aspects of performance. So I am half way there.

I am inspired by Maya Angelou.

"I've learnt that people will forget what you said, people will forget what you did, but people will never forget how you made them feel."

I start coaching from "the heart, not the chart" (an Eliza quote). Uninhibited, spontaneous unlike my natural reserved self, I enjoy the role of pitch coach. And seemingly so did CBRE. They called on me for over 10 years.

are you an actor?

No, but when you pitch you're on show.

I think 'if only she knew how shy I really am.'

I demonstrate with a degree of spontaneity totally alien to me. I allow my personality - unfettered - do the talking.

"You have to come across with emotion make them feel your passion"

"It's not what you say, It's the way you say it"

Imagine you are in a lift with someone you have only the time it takes to to the 7 floor to tell them your about

SOLUTION
PROBLEM
RESULTS

ENERGY
ENTHUSIASM

I decide to spread my newly found confidence by writing a self-help book on pitching. It is published in 7 languages and is helping people in both the USA and China.

I even have the confidence, based on a single wine-fuelled experience, to write a book about how to give the dream wedding speech. In it, I include my favourite quote by Picasso, "I am always doing that which I cannot do, in order that I may learn how to do it."

A perceptive review of my first book strikes home. "You even find how to get over yourself, perhaps the toughest pitch hurdle of all."

FOUNDLING

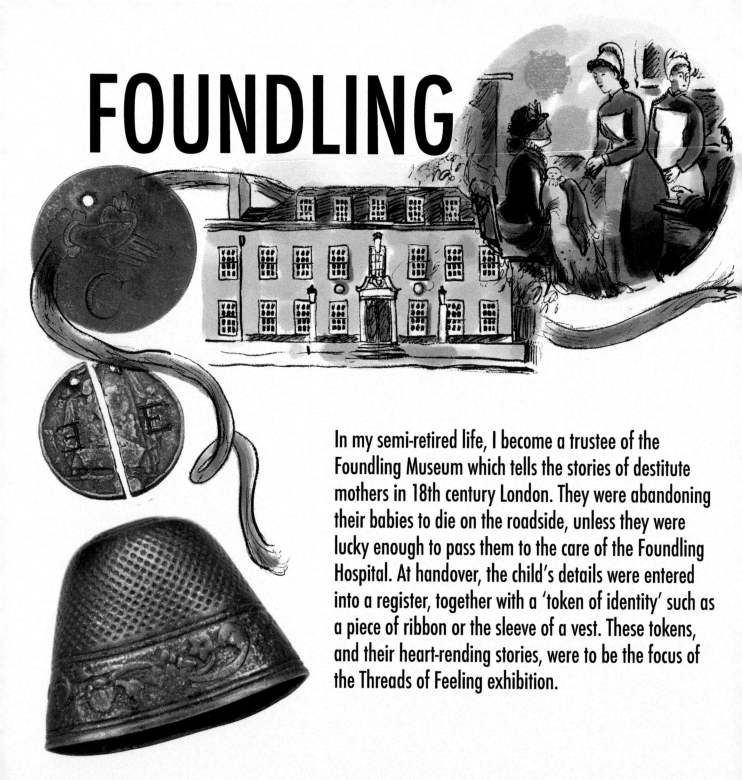

In my semi-retired life, I become a trustee of the Foundling Museum which tells the stories of destitute mothers in 18th century London. They were abandoning their babies to die on the roadside, unless they were lucky enough to pass them to the care of the Foundling Hospital. At handover, the child's details were entered into a register, together with a 'token of identity' such as a piece of ribbon or the sleeve of a vest. These tokens, and their heart-rending stories, were to be the focus of the Threads of Feeling exhibition.

There is no money in the kitty and no one to produce it. Trustees are voting to cancel the whole thing, so I volunteer to make it all happen. I find myself on a crusade.

John Styles, a noted historian, who is curating the exhibition, has a list of his non-negotiable requirements, seemingly impossible without money.

I need all my pitching skills. My weapon is the Foundling story. I tell it first to my daughter, Laura who loves that I'm doing something so worthwhile, (unlike advertising!) She designs a beautiful book to showcase the Threads. Armed with this, I recruit a team of volunteer 'threadies'.

Nick develops the distinctive identity and signage.

Annabelle sources thousands of yards of ribbon, replicating the originals

Louise a talented young soprano, now on the international stage, researches and learns and sings eighteenth century ballads. Sam a DJ records them onto a disc for sale.

Sarah who I bump into in Portobello road, designs and makes wonderful eighteenth century gowns.

Alex creates 'threads online' one of the first of its kind.

Rob generates unbelievable press coverage.

Threads of Feeling even tours the USA. It is the museum's most successful exhibition.

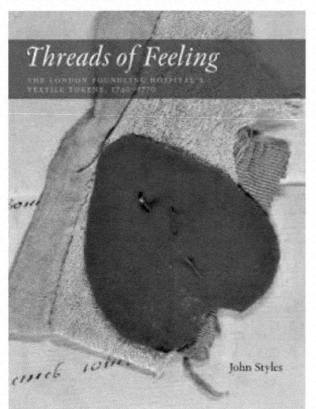

Threads of Feeling

THE LONDON FOUNDLING HOSPITAL'S
TEXTILE TOKENS, 1740–1770

John Styles

I spend six months working on 'Feeling'. Countless times, I tell the stories of the babies handed over to the Foundling, by despairing mothers whose only other option was to leave them by the roadside.

As I tell the stories, my thoughts turn again to my mother. She did not just wave goodbye as she handed me to the school on my fifth birthday, she was deeply upset - but never showed it. In a way she too had no option. It may not have been roadside abandonment, but social approbation was just as powerful.

At last, I can empathise, but too late, with her and the decision she took. It denied her, an instinctively good mother, much of the natural joy of motherhood. For me, the loss of intimacy was a catalyst to a lack of self-belief and the competitive need to prove myself.

At last, I understand myself better. I am less likely to find hurdles that are not real and so lucky to have Eliza keeping me 'honest' should I slide, and daughters who don't suffer foolishness gladly.
It is Hannah who suggests I write this life story.

LOCKDOWN POSTSCRIPT

I finish the last chapter in 2020.

COVID strikes, the worst disaster since WW2 when this memoir starts, being sent to boarding school on my fifth birthday.

In 1961, putting farm life behind me, I escape from the countryside to London. Now in 2021, I have escaped from London to the countryside. I feel I have come full circle physically and emotionally.

I replace the goal driven city routine with daily walks, reminiscent of training runs on Hampstead hills, with time to reflect and observe.

I replace farm labour with gentle gardening.

Cecily Salt lends her energetic pencil power to aid Michael's recollections, reimagining his 83 years on planet earth in engaging style.

A drawn line is free to explore in ways unconventional, piecing together memories, making sense of oneself, joining the dots - ultimately making something that is to some degree cathartic but also results in a readable memoir and keepsake.

By day, Cecily can be found running a screenprinting studio/shop in Ashburton Devon.

@cecilysalt

Acknowledgements

Page 37_38   The Sex Impulse and Achevement - 1922 ASHA physical-education poster (courtesy of Social Wefare History Archives, University of Minnesota Libraries)

Sexual Behaviour inthe Human Male A. Kinsey, W. Pomeroy, C. Martin published by W.B Saunders 1948

The Guide Through Boyhood educational booklet Father and Son Welfare Movement of Australia 1960

Life and Growth C.M. Legge and F.F. RigbyFaber and Faber Ltd published 1950

book covers public domain.

Page 057   National Service Barracks photo by Gary E Perkin / Alamy Stock Photo

Page 063   Charge of the Light brigade, 1855 painted by William Simpson Alamy stock photo

A rare shot of a 21 years old Winston Churchill in the uniform of the Fourth Queen's Own Hussars, 1895 CBW / Alamy Stock Photo

Page 96_97   Printing Press archive photo - Dave Bagnall Collection / Alamy Stock Photo

Printing Press archive photo - Black Country Images / Alamy Stock Photo

Page 115   Mexico olympics poster featuring Michael Parker

Page 116_117   John Carlos, Tommie Smith, Peter Norman 16th October 1968 Angelo Cozzi (Mondadori Publishers) Public Domain.

Page 150_154   Cover and Images from Threads of Feeling book, Foundling Museum. www.foundlingmuseum.org.uk

Page 155   Eliza Parker painting and back cover image www.elizaparkerart.com

Page 157_156   Cecily Salt www.cecilysalt.com